How to use this book

Follow the advice, in italics, given for you on each page.
Support the children as they read the text that is shaded in cream.
***Praise** the children at every step!*

Detailed guidance is provided in the Read Write Inc. Phonics Handbook

8 reading activities

Children:

- *Practise reading the speed sounds.*
- *Read the green and red words for the story.*
- *Listen as you read the introduction.*
- *Discuss the vocabulary check with you.*
- *Read the story.*
- *Re-read the story and discuss the 'questions to talk about'.*
- *Re-read the story with fluency and expression.*
- *Practise reading the speed words.*

Speed sounds

Consonants *Say the pure sounds (do not add 'uh').*

f	l	m	n	r	s	v	z	**sh**	th	ng
ff	**ll**	mm	nn	**rr**	ss	ve	zz			**nk**
			kn				s			

b	c	d	g	h	j	p	qu	t	w	x	y	ch
bb	k	dd	gg			pp		tt	wh			tch
	ck											

Vowels *Say the sounds in and out of order.*

at	hen	in	on	up	day	see	high	blow
	head					happy		

zoo	look	car	for	fair	whirl	shout	boy

*Each box contains one sound but sometimes more than one grapheme. Focus graphemes are **circled**.*

Green words

Read in Fred Talk (pure sounds).

shop must

smell dull tank stick

Read in syllables.

pa\`rrot → parrot in\`sect → insect vis\`it → visit

Red words

want you call we be No her are

Vocabulary check

Discuss the meaning (as used in the story) after the children have read each word.

	definition:
parrot	*brightly coloured bird*
stick insect	*a pet insect with long stick-like legs*
dull	*boring*
nip	*pinch*

Punctuation to note in this story:

Tab Meg Mum	*Capital letters for names*
No Can This Yes	*Capital letters that start sentences*
.	*Full stop at the end of each sentence*
?	*Question mark*

Tab the cat

Introduction

Have you ever begged your Mum and Dad for a pet?
What sort of pet would you like?

Meg wants a pet.
I wonder what pet she persuades her mum to buy?

Story written by Gill Munton
Illustrated by Tim Archbold

Mum and Meg are in the pet shop.

Can we get a fish?
No,
you must
get a big
tank if you
get a fish.

Can we get a stick insect?
No, a stick insect will be dull.

Can we get a parrot?
No, a parrot can nip you.

This cat wants you, Meg.

And I want her.

rrrrrrr

"I will call her Tab.

Tab the cat."

Questions to talk about

Re-read the page. Read the question to the children. Tell them whether it is a **FIND IT** *question or* **PROVE IT** *question.*

FIND IT

- ✓ *Turn to the page*
- ✓ *Read the question*
- ✓ *Find the answer*

PROVE IT

- ✓ *Turn to the page*
- ✓ *Read the question*
- ✓ *Find your evidence*
- ✓ *Explain why*

Page 8:	FIND IT	*Why did Mum not want to get a rat?*
Page 9:	FIND IT	*Why did Mum not want to get a fish?*
Page 10:	FIND IT	*Why did Mum not want to get a stick insect?*
Page 11:	FIND IT	*Why did Mum not want to get a parrot?*
Page 12:	PROVE IT	*Why do you think Mum was happy to get a cat?*